GOOD VEGGIE
BAD VEGGIE
I HATE ALL VEGGIES.

By: Rob Wiggz

WiggzWorks Publishing

A DIVISION OF WIGGZWORKS, LLC

Library of Congress control number: TXu 1-867-473
ISBN: 978-1-7353680-0-9

WiggzWorks, LLC is registered in U.S Patent and Trademark Office and Indiana Secratery of State.

Certain Trademarks are used under license.

Printed in United States.

WiggzWorks, LLC
www.wiggzworks.com
10203 Holly Berry Circle, Fishers, IN 46038

To my wife Cassandra and our kids, Darren, Quiara, and Makell.
Thank you for all your support and love.
I love you.

To the folks who are chasing their dreams, no matter what age, gender, or color you are, keep chasing them and you'll catch it soon.

"I'm just a dreamer from Curries Woods Public Housing of Jersey City, NJ, who expected nothing and worked hard for everything".

- Rob Wiggz

One veggie, two veggies, three veggies, four veggies,

Green veggies,

Yellow veggies,

I hate all veggies.

No matter what color, no matter what size,

No matter the texture

or taste I cry.

I hate all veggies,
I hate all veggies,

I cry, I cry, I hate all veggies.

Boiled or
steamed,

fried or grilled,
I hate all
veggies, warm or
chilled.

Veggies in a can, veggies in a bag,

veggies from the garden,
all veggies
are bad.

I hate all veggies,
I hate all veggies,

I cry, I cry, I hate all veggies.

Gives you
all the vitamins
you need for
the day,

help you see better

and run fast when you play.

Help you run fast and help you live long?

Yes, yes, and yes.
Veggies are best.

Here, try them with ranch,
try them with cheese.

I love carrots with ranch

and broccoli with cheese.

All veggies aren't bad,

give me more please.

Celery with peanut butter,

or rice with peas, stir-fried with chicken, give me more please.

Some veggies are good,
fried or grilled,

boiled or steamed,
warmed or chilled.

Some veggies are good, as a smoothie or in a bag,

I don't hate all veggies, all veggies aren't bad.

One veggie,
two veggies,
three veggies,
four veggies,

Green veggies, yellow veggies
I want more veggies.

No matter what color, no matter what size, no matter the texture or taste I cry,

Give me more, give me more,
I cry, I cry, give me more veggies.

CPSIA information can be obtained
at www.ICGtesting.com
Printed in the USA
LVHW071715200421
685033LV00010B/354

* 9 7 8 1 7 3 5 3 6 8 0 0 9 *